TYPEWRITING IDENTIFICATION (I.S.Q.T.)

Identification System for Questioned Typewriting

TYPEWRITING IDENTIFICATION (I.S.Q.T.)

Identification System for Questioned Typewriting

By

BILLY PRIOR BATES, A.B., M.G.A., LL.B.

CHARLES C THOMAS • PUBLISHER

Springfield • Illinois • U.S.A.

Published and Distributed Throughout the World by

CHARLES C THOMAS • PUBLISHER

BANNERSTONE HOUSE

301-327 East Lawrence Avenue, Springfield, Illinois, U.S.A.

NATCHEZ PLANTATION HOUSE

735 North Atlantic Boulevard, Fort Lauderdale, Florida, U.S.A.

With **THOMAS BOOKS** *careful attention is given to all details of manufacturing and design. It is the Publisher's desire to present books that are satisfactory as to their physical qualities and artistic possibilities and appropriate for their particular use.* **THOMAS BOOKS** *will be true to those laws of quality that assure a good name and good will.*

Printed in the United States of America
HH-11

Preface

LIKE handwriting identification, typewriting identification has two essential parts: *discovery* of the fact and *proof* of the fact.

The purpose of this manual is to put at the fingertips of the questioned document examiner, and the lawyer handling a questioned typewriting case, a scientific method for the discovery of the fact and the proving of it.

Part I of the manual, which treats typewriting identification with the I.S.Q.D.* principles applicable to handwriting identification, presents the scientific method of identifying a questioned typewriting.

Part II of the manual sets forth the examiner's preparation of the facts for his demonstration in court, and the method of presentation.

It is not within the scope of this manual to include identification from the typewriter ribbon, or from the paper on which the questioned typewriting is written. These aspects of the field are left to the examiner, or to a scientific identification technician, to handle.

In some cases, training in chemical problems is required, including the use of the spectrograph. And in dealing with erasures, for example, training is required in the use of special optical equipment and infrared and ultraviolet lights.

In this day of specialization and modern equipment, the average typewriting examiner is not expected to be an expert in all the technical laboratory methods available. It is im-

---

*Bates, Billy Prior: *I.S.Q.D. Identification System for Questioned Documents.* Springfield, Thomas, 1970.

portant, however, for him to know that these tests can be done for him by a scientific identification technician.

Attention in this manual is given only to the method used in comparing the *basic strokes* of a typewriting for its identification, and the preparation and presentation of these facts in court.

B.P.B.

Contents

Page

Preface v

PART I

DISCOVERY OF THE FACT

Section

  1. Principles Applicable to Handwriting Identification 5
  2. Individually of Machine 7
  3. Individuality of Operator 12
  4. Fraudulent Alterations 15
  5. Typewriting Reduced to Basic Strokes 18
  6. Method: Twelve Points of Comparison 19
  7. Conclusion 59
  8. Summary 60

PART II

PROOF OF THE FACT

Section

  1. Reasons and Basis for Opinion 63
  2. Forensic Photography 65
  3. Enlargements of Twelve Points of Comparison... 67
  4. Duplicate Photographs 72
  5. Markings on Photographs 74
  6. Photostatic Photographs 76
  7. Identification from Carbon Copies 78
  8. Mounting Exhibits 81
  9. Classification of Twelve Points of Comparison... 84
  10. Admissible as Evidence 87
  11. Presentation in Court of the Proof of the Fact ... 90
  12. Conclusion

Bibliography 94

Index 95

TYPEWRITING IDENTIFICATION (I.S.Q.T.)

Identification System for Questioned Typewriting

PART I

DISCOVERY OF THE FACT

Section 1

Principles Applicable to Handwriting Identification

QUITE often a questioned document examiner, or an attorney asked to handle a questioned document case, will shy away from questioned typewriting. But once he understands the principles underlying the identification of a questioned typewriting he can be as sure of his conclusion as he is of questioned handwriting.

Just as each person acquires certain identifiable characteristics in his handwriting, so does a typewriter. Through manufacture, constant use, and accident a machine acquires identifiable defects in its type face, alignment, and other points of comparison.

The principles underlying the identification of typewriting are the same as those underlying handwriting identification. The first step is to establish the standard and then, by a scientific comparison of all the elements and characteristics of the questioned with the standard, similarity or dissimilarity is established.

Just as in handwriting examination, a stroke by stroke study of a typewritten document is made. The trained examiner will be as keenly observant, and will give his attention to every detail, in the detection of fraud in typewriting as in handwriting.

In the I.S.Q.T. method of identification the analyst will consider points very similar to those considered in handwriting analysis. He will compare uniformity, spacing and alignment. He will measure the degree of slant, the weight, and the size and proportion of the strokes. And he will carefully catalogue all irregularities. These will be discussed in detail in Section 6.

Not only will the examiner's trained eye detect unusual individual characteristics, but, as in the case of handwriting, he will classify these features and, all together, they will constitute the basis for his conclusion. The mathematical probability of the same combination of characteristics divergent from the norm appearing in two typewriting machines is practically nil.

As shown in subsequent sections of this manual, the same method of preparing exhibits, and their admissibility and presentation in court, applies to questioned typewritten documents as to questioned handwritten documents.

Section 2

Individuality of Machine

IN A QUESTIONED typewriting case, perhaps the most important issue is whether the document was produced on a particular machine.

The first step for the examiner is to determine the fact that the given document was typed on a particular make of machine; second, he must determine the fact that the document was typed on a particular machine of that particular make.

Make of Machine

Of all the various makes and models of typewriting machines in existence no two are exactly alike. No manufacturer makes all the characters of his typewriter exactly the same as any other. Although these typewriting machines may resemble each other in general style, no two machines carry exactly the same type faces. And any one manufacturer may make a change in the type face of a new model of his particular brand of typewriter.

With so many different brands, and different models of brands, on the market today—together with those which have been discontinued, but which are still in existence for a forger or anonymous writer to use—it would be very difficult for an examiner to recognize spontaneously every model of every brand ever manufactured. It would not be practical to list or illustrate in a book every type face in existence, especially in a simplified manual like this one.

However, each typewriter manufacturing company maintains a complete file of all the type faces used on its make and models, including a record of changes, which is available to a questioned document examiner. This affords him authoritative reference material. Also, the FBI Laboratory maintains a file of sample impressions of styles of type of every make and model of typewriter ever manufactured. These, however, may not be available to the ordinary document examiner.

Regardless of the make of the individual machine the analyst is dealing with, the general principles underlying its mechanism are similar. Likewise, the general principles underlying the determination of the fact that a questioned document was written on a particular make of machine are similar.

An exception is the IBM Selectric machine, which employs a high-speed ball, called a "type-head," instead of the usual typebars that strike into an inked ribbon, as on the majority of machines. Because this type-head is completely interchangeable with other type-heads, allowing different styles of writing to be made by one machine (or the same style of writing made by several different machines), identification of the individual machine on which a questioned typewriting was made may not be possible.

However, since each type-head has its own distinctive

```
Little Monkey        Little Monkey

La Honda             La Honda

Ah-teen'             Ah-teen'

Redwoods             Redwoods

Creek                Creek

Cathedral            Cathedral

Rel                  Rel
```

Figure 1. Different styles of writing produced on one machine by different type-heads.

peculiarities and defects, identification of a particular type-head can be made.

Styles of Type

Although the variations in the design of type faces may be so slight that they are perceptible only under magnification, they may be the prevailing factors in the identification of an individual machine.

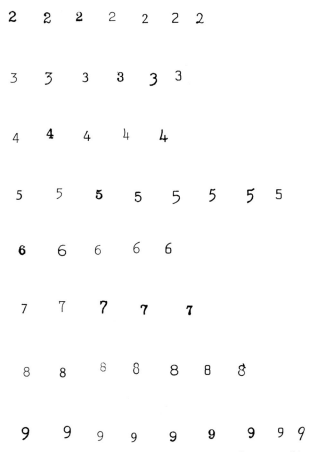

Figure 2. Distinguishing type styles of various machines.

An example is the manufacturer who changed the top portions of the small letter *m* from a flat to a saw-toothed design in order to reduce ink-clogging of the type face when a new ribbon was used—a slight change, but very significant for identification purposes.

The typewriter records its individuality in the documents it produces, its pecularities offering specific points of identification. Its distinctive character distinguishes it from all other machines.

Particular Machine

In some cases, it is easier to determine the fact that a typewriting was written on a certain particular machine than to establish the make of the machine. A few telltale charac-

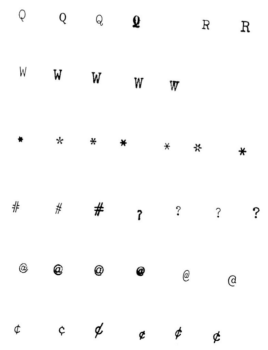

Figure 3. Distinguishing type styles of various machines.

teristics and defects appearing in both the questioned and standard exemplars are sometimes sufficient to identify a particular machine.

Differences in design and size and proportions of the type faces will also help to identify a particular machine. The length of a typewritten line, and the vertical spacing between lines are other factors in identification.

These points will be discussed in detail in Section 6.

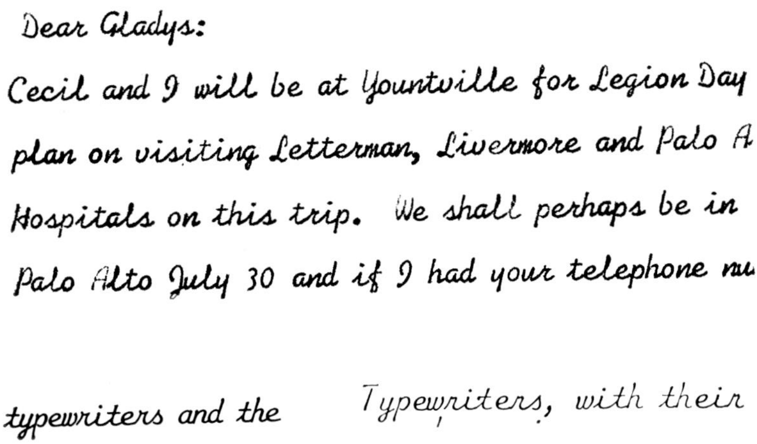

Dear Gladys:

Cecil and I will be at Yountville for Legion Day

plan on visiting Letterman, Livermore and Palo A

Hospitals on this trip. We shall perhaps be in

Palo Alto July 30 and if I had your telephone nu

typewriters and the   *Typewriters, with their*

Figure 4. Distinguishing styles of script.

Section 3

Individuality of Operator

THE examiner will not only want to identify the machine on which a document was written, but he will want to try to identify the person who wrote the document. Although it is not always possible to determine the operator of a typewriting machine, there are certain characteristics which will help to identify him.

Each typist has his own individual touch. A skilled examiner can often tell the difference between the touch of one person and another. Different typists vary in the force with which they strike the keys, resulting in a variation in the pressure on the paper.

Usually self-taught typists acquire an uneven touch and irregular speed, resulting in an inferior quality of typewriting. The nature of the impressions can often determine whether a questioned alteration or substitution was written by the same operator or by an operator different from the one who wrote the body of the document.

A semiskilled operator will often depress a key involving the use of the little fingers lighter than the other keys, because these fingers are not used as much as the others. An unskilled operator will very often strike a wrong key involving the use of the little fingers.

With a skilled operator, sometimes when the combination of certain letters are used one of the two letters lifts or drops out of alignment, due to the irregularity of the touch attributed to the speed of the operator (see Fig. 8).

Often it can be ascertained by the touch whether the operator was a professional speed typist or a proponent of the hunt and peck system. Of course if the specimen has been written on an electric typewriter, this element of identification is lost.

However, whether the touch-type or the sight method is employed, or if the specimen was written on an electric typewriter, certain characteristic irregularities—habits acquired by the typist—will appear in the typewriting. These peculiarities offer the investigator points of identification.

Among these peculiarities is the arrangement of the subject matter on the page. The location of the typewritten material in relation to the edges of the paper, how much margin he leaves on either side and at the top and bottom of the page, as well as paragraph indentation and other spacing, reflect the personal taste of the typist. These are often characteristic, especially when the typist is inexperienced and has no models of accepted business practice from which to copy.

Personal idiosyncracies will also crop up in the content of the subject matter itself. Certain colloquialisms, wording and construction of sentences, habits of punctuation, and the incorrect use of capitals, figures, or other characters, all will help to identify the operator of a typewriting machine. The use of the capital *I* for the figure *1,* or the use of & for *and,* are examples of personal idiosyncracies.

Spelling is another factor to be considered. Obviously a person can spell no better on a typewriter than by hand. In fact, additional misspelled words can usually be found

```
and to Renette Peters, $I5,000.
Because my mother and father were
sum of $I,000.  My neighbor and g
friend Stella Neuer, $500 for the
with the $I00 he owed Mr. Warren
Allen and Sue became Mr. and Mrs.
Allen Thomas Peters on August 23;
ing.
```

Figure 5. Use of the capital I for the figure 1.

in a typewritten document due to the lack of coordination of the typist. The consistent misspelling of certain words will sometimes trap the forger or anonymous letter-writer.

The identification of a typewriter operator is based primarily on the above factors. The extent to which proof of these points may establish identification of the operator depends upon the facts in each case. In some cases typewritten documents may be of a personal nature, making them more easily identifiable with their authors than in other cases.

```
I am plane disgussed
with the whole thing
& I won't stand it no
longer.
```

```
under the bench on the
left & in plane sight.
I will be waching & you
make sure their are no
policemens.
```

Figure 6. Identification by & sign.

Section 4

Fraudulent Alterations

Ever since the typewriter became the accepted means of producing commercial and legal papers, it has been a means of producing fraudulent documents. Because the forger has erroneously assumed that a typewriter has no individuality, and therefore its fraudulent character cannot be exposed, he has produced numerous fraudulent documents of various kinds.

In the case of a will, sometimes a forger will substitute whole fraudulent typewritten pages. In other cases, he may add a paragraph or an interlineation after the instrument has been duly executed. This type of modification is commonly found in deeds and contracts.

Modifications are also found in negotiable instruments, receipts, and other vouchers, where the forger has added to or altered the conditions. Figures, words, sentences, paragraphs, and even entire pages are altered or added to documents. Modifying clauses or sentences are sometimes interlined above signatures.

When a fraudulent alteration is suspected, the examiner will determine first whether or not the same machine was used (see I.S.Q.T. method, Part I, Sec. 6). Then, he will determine if the typewriting was produced by the same operator (Part I, Sec. 3). Not only will the examiner want to identify the person who made the change; he will want to determine when the change was made.

Determination of Date

The date of a typewriting in many cases can be established

and positively proved. Often it is important merely to ascertain the date of a typewritten document. In other cases, it may be important to determine whether or not a document was written continuously in one operation, or written at different times. And if the document was written at different times, there is the question as to whether it was written at different times on the same machine or at different times on different machines.

If a specimen indicates it was not written in one continuous operation, there is reason to suspect fraud, for an authoritative document should have been typewritten in one continuous operation.

An interruption in the typewriting may be shown by a dissimilarity in the line spacings, a dissimilarity in the vertical alignment of the individual letters and of the margins. A difference in the parallelism of the lines is also an indication that the document had been removed and reinserted in the machine. Each line should be exactly parallel to and equidistant from the line above it.

In ascertaining the genuineness of a typewritten document the make and model of machine, with its characteristic style of type faces, may establish the approximate date of the writing. Typewriters of the various makes and models were not manufactured before certain dates, and styles of type have been improved or changed periodically, dating a typewriter.

A record of changes in styles of type faces, listing the year and the manufacturer, is a valuable aid to the examiner in determining the date of a questioned typewriting.

Defects in the impressions on the typewritten document offer another means of determining the approximate date on which a certain typewriter was used to write a certain document. New defects appear in the type faces from time to time which will remain, or become more prominent, in the impressions. By comparing the questioned document with authentic documents obtained from records and other sources, the examiner may ascertain the approximate time the questioned document was prepared.

The type faces of many letters become worn and damaged through use. With successive dated specimens of writing produced by a machine available for comparison, the examiner can show with absolute certainty when specific defects first appeared.

Because the defects and irregularities in type faces develop gradually, standards should include some made at the time the document purports to have been prepared as well as some written at later dates. The more specimens an examiner obtains the more apparent the history becomes, and the closer his estimate of the date. A typewriter makes a continuous record of its own history, and when an adequate amount of continuous typewriting is available the dates of typewriting can be established.

Section 5

Typewriting Reduced to Basic Strokes

TYPEWRITING, like handwriting, can be broken down into two fundamental strokes—the straight stroke, or *bar,* and the *curve.*

The I.S.Q.T. system of identification is based on the scientific analysis of these two strokes, and the direction in which they take to form the individual letters, numbers, and other characters that constitute typewriting.

It is through the combination of these basic strokes that typewriting is constructed. For example, three bars are combined in one way to form the letter *H,* and in another way to form the letter *Y.* Two curves are combined to form an *O* and two bars and a curve are combined to form a *U.*

The strokes of a questioned typewriting are weighed in their relationship to the rest of the strokes in the body of the same document, or with those strokes in a separate standard, with which the examiner is making his comparison.

In this method of examination, questioned typewriting identification is placed on the same laboratory basis as fingerprint identification.

Section 6

Method: Twelve Points of Comparison

JUST as in the scientific examination of a handwriting, the first step in the examination of a questioned typewriting is to observe its general appearance.

Upon careful observation, obvious similarities and differences between the questioned and the standard typewriting will be apparent; conspicuous characteristics and irregularities will be noticeable. By a breakdown of the typewriting stroke by stroke, the inconspicuous characteristics will be detected. Every single stroke, including punctuation marks, must be thoroughly examined for clues. Nicked or worn type faces are powerful clues.

The following method of making a scientific comparison, stroke by stroke, of a questioned typewriting with the genuine, places typewriting identification on a laboratory basis. No matter in which laboratory the examination is made, or by which trained examiner it is made, the conclusion will hold true.

POINT 1: UNIFORMITY

When the examiner observes the appearance of the type-written exemplars in the case he is handling, he will note the quality of the typewriting. Good quality typewriting produces uniformity in a specimen.

Dirty type faces, or excessive ink in the ribbon, will give the typewriting a smudged appearance.

The analyst will look for uniformity in the arrangement of the subject matter on the page, such as its location in rela-

```
The male is less evolved than
the female/ He hasm't entirel
oytgrown his playboy flag-wavj
And when he isn't waving a fle
```

Figure 7. Uniform appearance of untidiness.

tion to the edges of the paper, and the consistency in width of margins, paragraph indentations and other spacing.

The analyst will also look for uniformity in the weight of the typewritten strokes. Irregular speed and an uneven touch result in an inferior quality of typewriting. Some of the strokes will be lighter than others.

Inferior typewriting may contain strikeovers throughout the subject matter, giving the specimen a uniform appearance of untidiness.

Another feature of quality in the uniformity of typewriting is the alignment of the letters and figures in relation to the baseline of the writing. If the strokes appear above or below the baseline, the writing will appear unbalanced.

When a typewriter is new, or is properly adjusted, all parts of its type face print clearly and uniformly. The imprints, the spacing, and the inking of the typing are all uniform. As a typewriter is used, defects in the type face come into the

```
            ↓
    belligerent and animalistic.
    The Statue of Liberty and nov
    the Statue of Responsibility.
    for the rest.  Why?  Because
            ↑
```

```
        ↓              ↓
    So We've followed him
    in there.  How will it
    around here. ↑As for t
```

Figure 8. Unbalanced appearance.

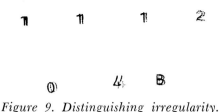

Figure 9. Distinguishing irregularity.

picture spoiling the uniformity. These defects will be discussed under Irregularities immediately following.

POINT 2: IRREGULARITIES

Although the type faces of a machine which is new are usually free of irregularities, or defects, it is possible for defects to occur in the castings or in the assembling of the machine. Defects can also occur by way of breakage in accidents. However, by far the most common cause of irregularities is the natural wear of the machine. Type faces become worn, battered, or broken by use, leaving marks, dents and scars.

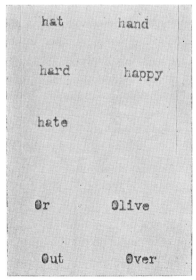

Figure 10. Distinguishing irregularity.

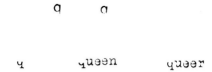

The pajamas were stashed quickly

Figure 11. Distinguishing defects.

The gradual deterioration of the type faces, together with any slight imperfections they may have had to begin with, produce unique characteristics—irregularities—in the typewriting. These abnormal characteristics distinguish the work of that individual machine from the work of any other machine, even of the same make.

Defects in the type faces are progressive, new ones making their appearance from time to time. Once they appear they will remain permanently, or will become enlarged and more prominent.

A major cause of defects through wear and tear is the typist

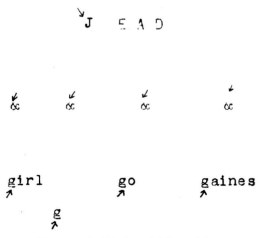

Figure 12. Distinguishing defects.

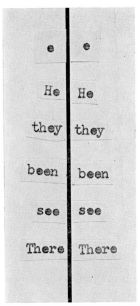

Figure 13. Defective e; no amount of cleaning will remove smudge.

depressing two keys at approximately the same time, the type face of the second character striking the back of the first type bar. This creates a slight scar on the face of the second character, which will become more pronounced with continued use.

Especially vulnerable to wear and tear are the serifs—the embellishments on the type—which become distorted through the use and abuse of a typewriter.

Sometimes the slender bars that operate the type become warped or loose through constant use, or through extra force by the operator in manipulating the keys, causing irregularities in the typewriting.

Figure 14. Defective serifs.

Muddiness in a typewritten specimen is another irregularity to consider in making an identification. The filling in of certain letters, as illustrated in Figure 15, caused by the collection of lint and other dirt in the cavities of the type faces, gives the characters a muddy look. The dirt prevents a complete imprint, much like that caused by a defect in the type face.

Muddy printing should be examined carefully to determine whether it was caused by faulty type faces or a faulty ribbon. A smudged appearance can be caused by an excessive amount of ink in the ribbon. In this case, the overall characters will be muddy. When the type faces are dirty, usually only certain characters are filled in.

Irregularities are not confined to the machine itself; they may be caused by the operator as well. As it was pointed out in Section 3, every typist leaves his own individuality and idiosyncracies—characteristic irregularities—in his typewriting. These the examiner will include in his analysis of the typewritten specimens.

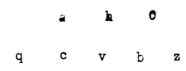

Figure 15. Only certain characters on same machine are muddy.

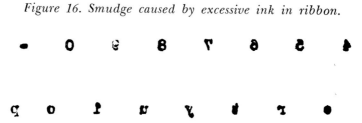

Figure 16. Smudge caused by excessive ink in ribbon.

Figure 17. Back of page showing bleeding through of excessive ink in ribbon.

An irregularity may be caused by the operator in his per-petration of the fraud. When he attempts to alter a number, for example, he will find it very difficult to cover the original figure completely with his overtyping on another machine. Although numbers are similar on the different machines, there is sufficient difference to distinguish them (see Fig. 95).

Not all irregularities are noticeable to the naked eye. Therefore all typewriting under the scrutiny of an investi-gator should be submitted to microscopic examination.

Irregularities are definite factors of identification. If the characters show specific irregularities in sufficient number in the questioned typewriting, and the same is found in the work of a particular machine, the identity is established.

POINT 3: SIZE AND PROPORTION

In typewriting examination, the style of the characters is the first and probably the principal factor in identifica-tion. Each style of type is distinctive, thereby identifying the machine used to write a certain document, and distin-guishing the typewriting from that done on other typewriters.

Each style of type, like the pica or the elite, has a definite size and proportion of type face. And the several makes and models of machines carrying pica or elite type have them-selves different designs of type faces, all having a definite size and proportion.

Although the various typewriter manufacturers follow a style similar in general features, there is a distinct individ-uality of design. For example, some of the capital or lower

how to play with the

how to play with the

how to play with the

Figure 18. Proportional type compared with regular type.

case letters are wider or narrower in one design than in another. Proportional type, based on the size of the letters instead of the number of letters to the inch, which is used on certain kinds of machines, is quite distinctive.

A precision ruler should be used to measure the overall height and width of each typewritten letter and number, as well as the height and width of the individual strokes that form them. Measurement of the individual strokes is discussed under Points 9 and 10—Bars and Curves.

Attention should also be paid to characters other than

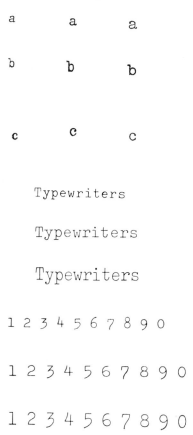

Figure 19. Variation in size and proportion of type.

Figure 20. Variation in style, size and proportion.

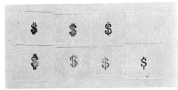

Figure 21. Variation in length of bars, space between bars, and size and proportion of "S."

Figure 22. Variation in size and curvature.

Figure 23. Variation in length and width.

numbers and letters of the alphabet. Symbols like & and $ are distinctive and have a definite size and proportion. Parentheses differ in size and curvature, and hyphens differ in length and width.

Every typewritten character, and every basic stroke forming a character, in the questioned typewriting can be measured and compared with its counterpart in the standard. Measurement of the size and proportion of the individual strokes in relation to the other strokes of the same typewriting, or to the strokes of the typewriting in the exemplar with which it is being compared, will help to establish the identity of the typewriting and the machine on which it was written.

POINT 4: ALIGNMENT

In the usual machine, type faces are made concave to conform to the curve of the platen which serves as the printing

```
meet me at the produce
market on Friday/ The
carrots were sold by the
case/ Carter took 3, Neuer 5,
Wells 6, Lewis 7, and
Logan 9/
```

Figure 24. Work of an old machine showing misalignment.

surface. When a typewriter is new, or is in proper adjustment, all parts of these type faces print uniformly. All the characters in relation to adjacent characters are in perfect horizontal and vertical alignment with the baseline of the writing.

With continued use, one or more characters will print slightly above or below the horizontal baseline of the other characters, or will diverge from their perfect vertical alignment in relation to adjacent characters. These divergences from exact horizontal and vertical alignment produce an individuality in the typewriting which is an important element in identification.

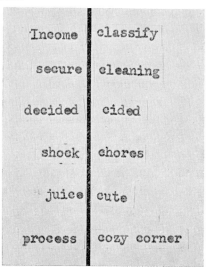

Figure 25. Identification by misalignment of c.

Figure 26. Typewriting characters occupying imaginary squares.

In typewriting, each character occupies an imaginary square. When a character is in perfect alignment it will be in the exact middle of this imaginary square; when out of alignment, it will be located above or below, or to the left or right, of the middle position. Even when only a part of the character is printed, the impression may show where the type is out of alignment.

When the divergence is great it can be easily seen, but sometimes the malalignment is so slight it is necessary to use magnification in making the measurement. Of course, the value in the alignment point of identification is the frequency of certain characters being out of alignment.

A faulty machine is not the only cause of misalignment in the writing. The operator of the machine is another factor to consider. Although an experienced typist may be skillful in the reinsertion of a sheet of paper into the machine, it is difficult to replace the sheet in the exact location it occupied during the original typing.

By ruling the sheet vertically the examiner will find, if

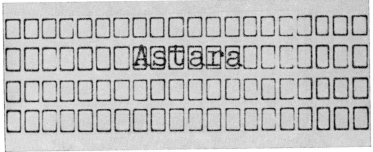

Figure 27. Typewriting photographed with template to show alignment.

there has been a reinsertion, that the characters are not all lined up directly under each other as they would be if the writing had been done in one continuous operation.

A horizontal ruling of the sheet will show whether or not all the characters are in alignment with each other along the baseline of the writing.

An exception to the rule that all the characters in a typewriting produced in one continuous operation are lined up directly under each other is found when the machine is one

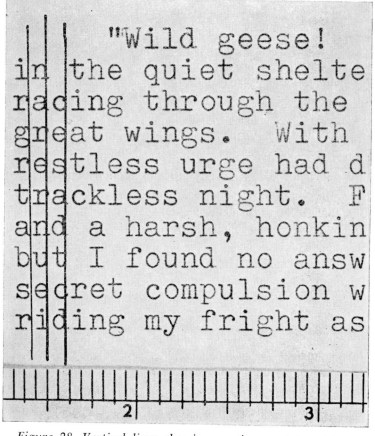

Figure 28. Vertical lines showing continuous typewriting.

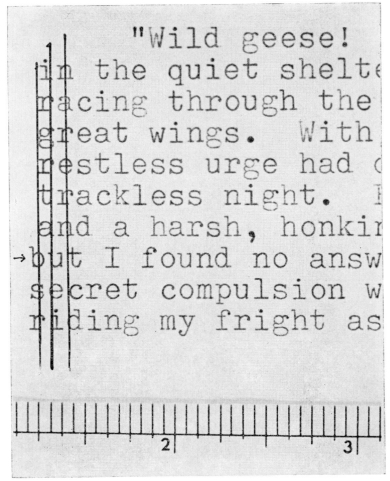

Figure 29. Vertical lines showing misalignment due to reinsertion of page.

with proportoinal type, like the IBM Executive typewriter. In this case, each individual character is given a variable spacing. The letter *i*, for example, has just as much space on each side of it as the letter *m*, and does not have a pinched or cramped appearance. This style of type is easily recognized,

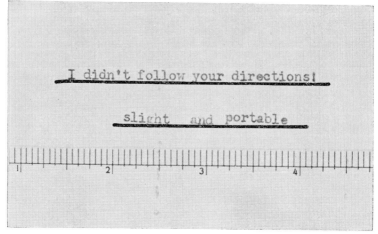

Figure 30. Horizontal lines showing misalignment due to faulty machine.

and must be taken into consideration in questions of alignment.

Improper alignment may also be caused by the irregular touch and speed of the operator. When certain letters are struck in combination by some typists, one of the two letters will lift or drop out of alignment with the baseline (Fig. 8).

Whether due to a faulty machine, or to the operator of the machine, consistent misalignment of one or more characters in a typewriting is a valuable aid to identification.

POINT 5: SPACING

Identification by the spacing in a typewriting entails two factors: (a) the spacing of the characters on the page caused by the habits of the operator, and (b) the spacing of the characters caused by the individual machine.

The operator will determine the amount of space between the edges of the paper and the subject matter of the questioned document—that is, the width of the margins at the top, bottom and both sides of the page—which the investigator will measure and compare with the standard.

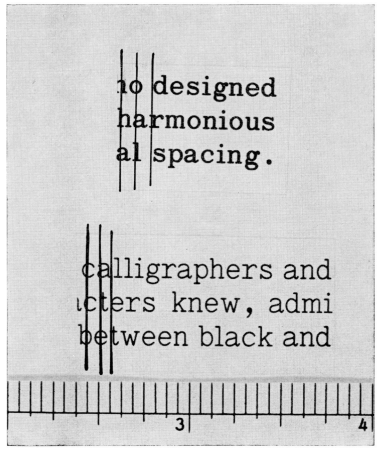

Figure 31. Normal misalignment in proportional type.

The investigator will also measure the number of spaces the operator has used in his paragraph indentations. Habits of indentation may be especially significant in identifying the author of an anonymous letter. For example, the fact that an anonymous letter contains six space-indentations may be an important factor in identifying its author. Recently, some editors have required six space-indentations, instead of the usual five, in the manuscripts they accept for publication.

```
uty, the         ant, is
ing, but         ed, conf
er, shoul
rmy, want        sen, I

                 lle, ret
```

```
eet. Los         ses.  I
nce. I           up.  Heav
on. She
bed. I           re. A com

                 ers.  "Ols
```

Figure 32. (Left) no space after commas, only one space after periods; work of inexperienced typist; (right) normal spacing after commas and periods.

A writer who is in the habit of following such a requirement may give himself away by typing an anonymous letter using six space-indentations.

The irregular spacing of the subject matter on the page, or of the individual characters, will also give away an inexperienced typist. One who has no knowledge of accepted business practice, with no model to follow, will be detected, as well as one who, for example, consistently leaves no space after his commas, or leaves only one space after his periods.

```
      "Off to war!"  a deep male voice
 in derision.  The women, dressed in a
 and lugging heavy sutcases, marched t
 Building, their heels pecking the gr:
  awoke to a breakfast of juicy sausage
 drilling up and down the platform wh:
 enlisted women to talk to the soldier
 world to ride my geese and see how fa
 if I dare to go?
```

Figure 33. Irregular spacing between lines.

As pointed out in Point 4 (Alignment), where additions or alterations have been made it is difficult for even a skilled operator to reinsert a sheet into the machine. Spacing will not match precisely. Measurement will reveal whether or not the space between each written line is exactly the same.

The spacing between the letters and words of a line is also important. Limited space forces cramped typewriting. The substituted writing in a fraudulent alteration may require more space than the forger anticipated, resulting in irregular spacing.

Differences in spacing are also caused by the individual machine. There are two different systems of spacing the characters in typewriting. Most machines use the block system in which each character occupies an imaginary square. In this system, which allows the same amount of space for all characters, some of the characters must necessarily be very close to the adjacent ones. To compensate for this variation in spacing the size of some characters is increased.

The other system of spacing the characters on a machine is that of proportional type, in which each individual character is given variable spacing. Each character is printed symmetrically in relation to every other character on the machine, regardless of the number of characters measured to the inch (see Fig. 31).

```
on K.P. in V irginia.
Wood's Lake in the pines,
onions. Ree.  Jeepers!
```

```
when you consider the Heart Seed Atom.

when you consider the Heart Seed Atom.
```

Figure 34. Irregular spacing between letters and words.

wh   wh   wh   wh
wh   wh   wh   wh

th   th   th   th
th   th   th   th

Figure 35. Variation in spacing between adjacent letters within the block system.

Individual machines will also produce differences in spacing between the characters within the block system of typewriting. Certain letters adjacent to each other may be consistently close together in one specimen and spaced farther apart in the specimen with which it is being compared.

Differences in spacing caused by the machine may be due to the design of type in that particular make or model, or may be due to a slight imperfection in the manufacturing, or defects caused by use or accident. A bent or warped type bar, for example, will cause irregular spacing between the characters.

All irregularities in the spacing of a questioned typewriting should be noted by the examiner and measured and compared with the standards.

POINT 6: DEGREE OF SLANT

Typewriters are so constructed that each character must be printed perpendicular to the baseline of the typewriting, and parallel to each adjacent character. When the characters diverge (tilt) from the perpendicular position the irregularity is known as *slant*.

Determination of the degree of slant in a typewriting is important in individualizing a machine. Even when machines are new they are not perfect in this regard, and are distinguishable by this point. This is a characteristic that is usually permanent and continuous, and is not substantially changed in the manipulation of the keys by the typist.

As a typewriter wears, certain characters will show a decided slant to the left or right of the true vertical. This irregularity may be due to a mechanical defect of the character, or of the type bar to which it is attached. Even a slight warping, or looseness, of a bar may be enough to cause the type to strike out of the vertical position, and will help to identify the machine.

In some incidences, the degree of slant in the type design may help in an identification. For example, the / character may be distinguished by its degree of obliquity.

Slant may also be caused by the operator of a machine. The type bars may become bent or loose from excessive force in the manipulation of the keys, or from conflict of the type.

Whatever the cause, the degree of slant of the characters is a significant point in determining the identity of the machine, the operator, or the typewriting, and should be measured with the proper instruments.

A typewriting protractor is used to measure the degree of

Figure 36. Decided slant of letter w.

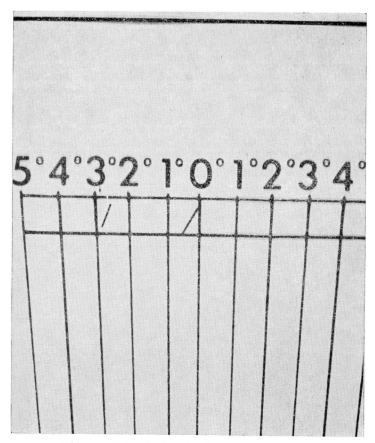

Figure 37. Variation in degree of obliquity.

slant. If the slant divergence is slight, it may go undetected until a transparent typewriting protractor is superimposed on the writing and the degree of slant is revealed.

POINT 7: WEIGHT OF STROKES

The weight of the strokes constituting the type characters is often the deciding factor in a typewriting identification.

In the I.S.Q.T. system, weight of the characters has two aspects: (a) the shading, or thickness of the strokes, and (b) the impressions made by the striking force of the keys.

When a typewriter is new, the weight of the characters is close to perfect, but the continued impact of the type character on the paper during the process of typewriting will eventually cause certain strokes of the character to strike harder than other parts. The result is a character comparatively heavy on its upper, lower, right or left side. It is "off its feet."

The footing of a typewriting—i.e. how the type stands "on its feet" or "off its feet," will help to identify a particular machine.

Shading, or thickness of strokes may also help to identify a particular machine, or a typewriting, with its distinctive design of type. Especially conspicuous is the shading of the type produced by the IBM typewriter. In this design of type the characters are slightly heavier in weight (thickness) in some places than in others. The distinctive design of IBM typewriting, with its proportional spacing, is easily identifiable. The shaded type faces will produce a consistently variable weight in the overall writing.

Defective type faces, excessive ink in the ribbon, and

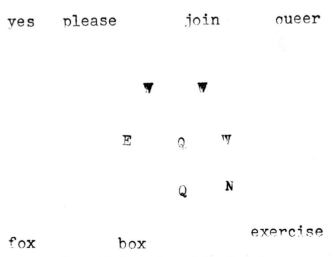

Figure 38. Irregular weight of strokes.

QUESTIONED   **STANDARD**

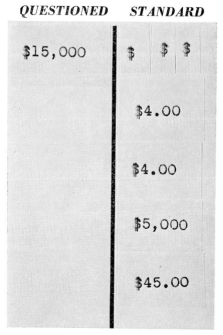

Figure 39. Identification by irregular weight of $.

Mike and Rea   IBM
Rob
Poon Yung Jung   Dee

                               Heidi

Figure 40. Normal shading of IBM typewriter.

dirt or lint accumulated in the crevices of the type, will also produce variable weight in the strokes, identifying a machine or a typewriting.

Characters in typewriting, like those in handwriting, may consist of fine strokes, medium, or heavy strokes.
These can be gauged with any straight edge ruler designed for precision measurement.

The second aspect of the weight of strokes—the impressions made by the striking force of the keys—is dependent upon

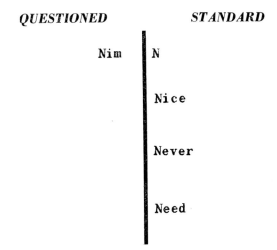

QUESTIONED   **STANDARD**

Nim | N

Nice

Never

Need

Figure 41. Identification by shaded type face of N.

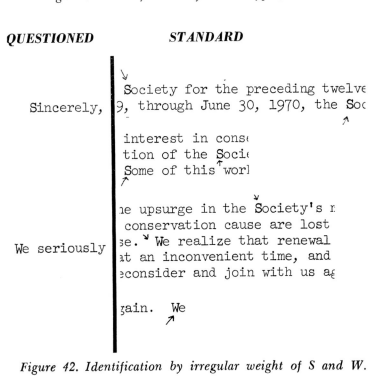

QUESTIONED   **STANDARD**

Sincerely,

Society for the preceding twelve
9, through June 30, 1970, the Soc

interest in cons(
tion of the Soci(
Some of this worl

We seriously

ιe upsurge in the Society's r
conservation cause are lost
ɜe. We realize that renewal
ιt an inconvenient time, and
ɜconsider and join with us aɜ

ɜain. We

Figure 42. Identification by irregular weight of S and W.

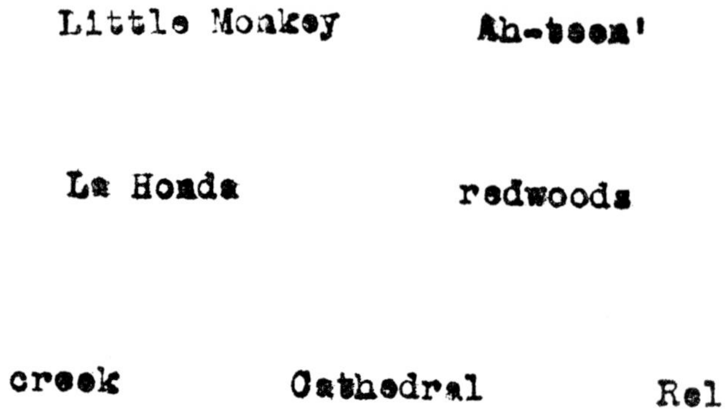

Little Monkey   Ah-teen'

La Honda   redwoods

creek   Cathedral   Rel

Figure 43. Variable weight due to excessive ink in ribbon and dirty type faces.

t

Figure 44. Fine strokes.

h

Figure 45. Medium strokes.

r

Figure 46. Heavy strokes.

the operator of the machine. Although this aspect of identification by the weight of the characters is lost when the work was produced on an electric typewriter with its uniform impression, the manually operated typewriter offers the examiner another factor of identification.

As shown in Section 3, each typist has his own individual touch. Depending upon the skill of the typist, and whether he used the touch system or the hunt and peck system, the resulting type impressions will be light, medium or heavy. The hunt and peck system is employed with more force by the operator, and the impressions will be heavier and uneven. There will be a variation in character shading where the operator hit the keys hard and where he hit them lighter.

Excessive force applied by the operator may result in the periods, commas, and certain other characters leaving burs on the back of the paper.

Other factors will also affect the weight of the strokes, such as a faulty platen and the ribbon of the machine. A dented platen will cause an uneven weight of strokes, and an inferior quality or worn ribbon will cause overall light impressions. A ribbon defective or worn in certain spots will create a variable weight in the strokes.

The examiner should check the exemplar to determine if the ribbon intensity is equal throughout the specimen. A change in the weight at one point in the writing, which continues from that point on, will show there was a lapse of time before the writing was continued.

Whatever the cause, when the weight of the characters of a certain portion of a typewriting is different from the body of the typewritten specimen—whether in thickness of strokes, or heaviness of impression—fraudulent alterations, interlineations, and additions can be detected and identified.

The weight of strokes can often help to identify a typewriting, the machine on which it was written, and the operator of the machine.

POINT 8: I-DOTS, PERIODS, COMMAS, QUOTATION MARKS

Seemingly insignificant, an i-dot, period, or comma may be the deciding factor in identifying a machine, its operator, or a specimen of typewriting.

Although the design of i-dots and periods in the various makes and models of machines is similar, a careful examination will reveal slight differences. A square-shaped period may be obvious to the casual observer, but not so obvious are those which are egg-shaped.

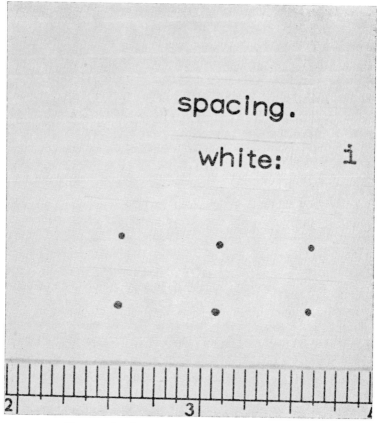

Figure 47. Square, round, egg-shaped dots.

Periods and i-dots should be examined under magnification to detect any slight difference in their design. Not only the shape of the dot should be observed—e.g. if it is round like a circle, or oval—but its size and weight should be noted. A very heavy or light dot will help make an identification.

i

Figure 48. Variation in size and weight of dots.

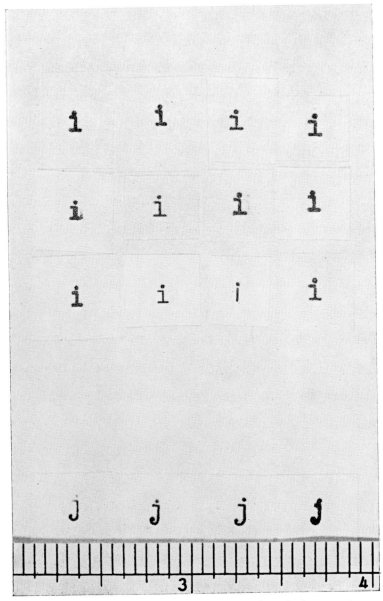

Figure 49. Variation in position of dot in relation to stem.

The position of the dot in relation to the stem of the *i* (and *j*) also varies with the design of type. Some are in direct line with the stem, while others are to the side of the stem at varying distances.

The position of the component parts of the colon and semicolon should also be studied, as well as their size, weight and shape.

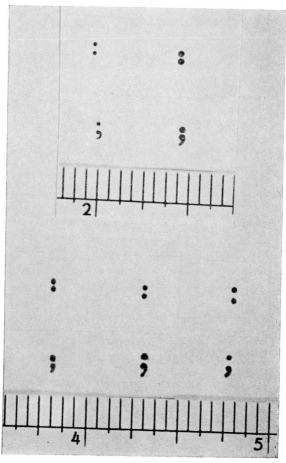

Figure 50. Variation in size, weight, shape, and space between imprints.

Commas also vary with different machines. Since the variation may be very slight, like i-dots and periods they should be submitted to magnification.

Enlargement will reveal significant differences. By reducing the comma to its basic strokes, the examiner will find, for example, whether the tail is blunt or pointed. He should also compare the size, shape and weight of the ball part of the comma in all specimens.

Like the comma, quotation marks, apostrophes, and exclamation marks vary with the machine and should be compared under magnification as to size, weight and shape.

Changing a period to a comma is one of the oldest tricks of a forger in making fraudulent alterations. It is not too difficult to change a period to a comma in a will, for ex-

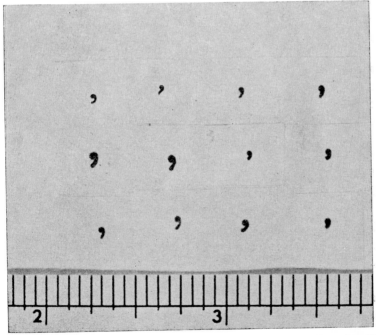

Figure 51. Variation in size, weight and shape of ball and tail of commas.

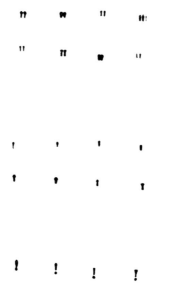

Figure 52. Variation in size, weight and shape of quotation marks, apostrophes and exclamation marks.

ample, and make what appears to be a continuation of a typewritten line. Therefore, the investigator should examine every comma, scrutinizing the ball and tail of each under magnification.

Periods and commas should also be studied in relation to the habits of the author of a questioned document (see Part I, Sec. 3). Punctuation in typewriting can be an important factor in identifying the operator of a machine.

Frequently the period and comma are misused by a forger in making alterations in sums of money. The habitual use of a comma to represent the decimal point, for example, will help to establish a fraud and identify the operator.

As shown in Point 5 *(Spacing)*, the habit of an operator of leaving no space after a comma, or of leaving only one space after a period, will identify him.

All characteristics of the i-dot, period, comma and quotation marks—their type design, defects in the type face, and their misuse by the operator—should be carefully noted by the examiner.

POINT 9: BARS

One of the two basic strokes into which typewriting can be broken down is the straight stroke—or bar—the other being the curve.

Almost all the letters, and many of the numbers and symbols, of typewriting are composed of bars. Some of the characters are composed solely of bars.

Some of the characters contain bars which serve as a staff onto which curves are attached.

—   /

Figure 53. Single bars representing certain symbols.

T   N   E   H   A

x   v   k

w

Figure 54. Two or more bars combined to form letters.

P   D   e   r

Figure 55. Single bar, single curve combined.

B

Figure 56. Single bar, two curves combined.

4   n   m

Figure 57. Two or more bars, one or more curves combined.

In reducing the type characters to their basic straight strokes, the investigator will be able to note the manner in which the strokes are connected to other straight strokes or to curves. He will measure the angle at which the strokes are joined, the distance from the baseline to the point were the strokes are joined, and the length of each individual bar. In measuring a bar's length, the serifs are not included.

The t-bar in typewriting, as in handwriting, can be a telltale stroke. The examiner should note the length and weight of the bar, how far up the staff it crosses, and whether the bar extends equidistant from each side of the staff, to the right of it, or to the left of it as in the case of a broken or defective t-bar.

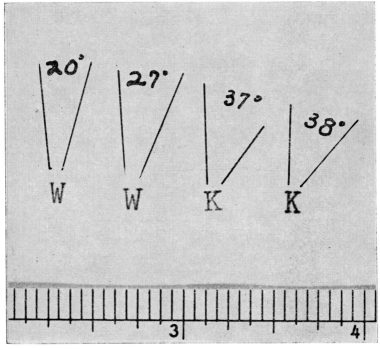

Figure 58. Angle at which strokes are joined.

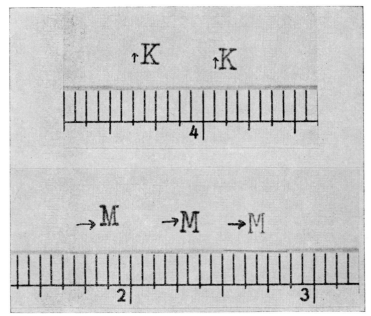

Figure 59. Distance from baseline to point where strokes are joined.

H   H   X   X

Figure 60. Length of individual bars.

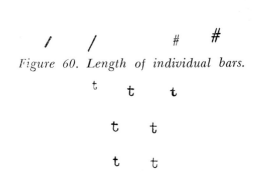

Figure 61. Variation in length and weight of t-bar, and its position in relation to the staff.

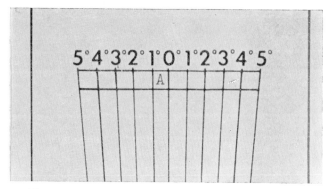

Figure 62. Measurement showing degree of slant.

As shown in Point 6, determination of slant in a typewriting is important in making an identification. The degree of slant is achieved by measuring the component bars of the character.

When the examiner establishes the habit of seeing the individual characters of typewriting in terms of their component parts—in this case, bars—he will find it easier to measure their size and proportion, their weight, and to detect any irregularities and defects.

POINT 10: CURVES

By reducing typewriting to its basic strokes it will be found that the majority of numbers and lower case letters, as well as nearly half of the capital letters, are composed of curves.

C

Figure 63. Single curve.

D

Figure 64. Single curve attached to bar.

$ $ ¢

Figure 65. Bars and curves combined in different ways.

R   R   R

Figure 66. Variation in design of curves in lower parts of first two letters; absence of curve in last letter.

4   4   4

Figure 67. Variation in design of curves in first two numbers; absence of curves in last letter.

0   0   0

Figure 68. Two curves combined to form different style zero in first two characters; four curves combined with bars to form zero in last character.

Figure 69. (Left) zero and capital O from same machine (similar); (right) zero and capital O from same machine (dissimilar).

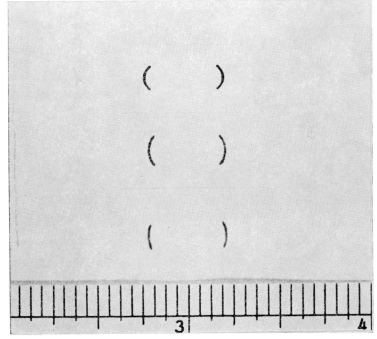

Figure 70. Difference in degree of concavity of curve.

As was shown in Point 9, some of these curves were attached to one or more bars. By reducing the characters to their basic components, the examiner will see the way in which each curve is joined to its adjacent stroke.

He should measure the size and proportion of each curve, the weight of the stroke, and look for any irregularities and defects in it. The difference in the shape of one curve alone, or the absence of a curve, could be an important factor in identifying a particular machine by its design of type.

( ) ( ) ( )

Figure 71. Difference in size and proportion (length) of curve.

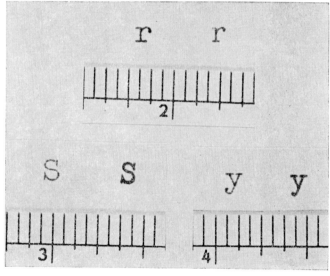

Figure 72. Difference in size of curve.

Q

Figure 73. Curve detached from curve.

Q

Figure 74. Curve attached to curve.

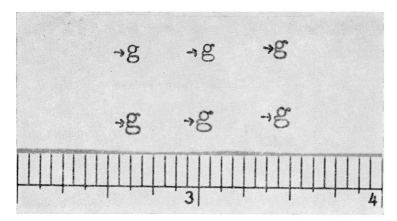

Figure 75. Difference in shape of curve joining the two circle formations.

POINT 11: CIRCLE FORMATIONS

Closely related to curves are circle formations. Whereas in handwriting a circle is a single curved line occurring at the baseline, in printing—and typewriting is a form of printing—a circle is two curves combined.

A circle formation may appear as a single character, it may be attached to a bar, or, as in the case of the *Q*, it is combined with a curve or bar which may be either attached or detached. Two circle formations may be combined in different ways to form a single character, like the letter *g* and the number *8* found in most styles of type, and the % symbol.

° o O

Figure 76. Circle formations as single characters.

p d b

Figure 77. Circle formations attached to bars.

g

Figure 78. Two circle formations joined by a curve.

Figure 79. Two circle formations separated by a bar.

%   %

Figure 80. Two circle formations separated by a bar, one circle joined to a curve.

%

Figure 81. Two circle formations separated by a bar, one circle joined to a short bar.

Circle formations vary in design according to the make and models of the machine. Some are perfectly round, like the upper part of the *g*, while others are oval as in the lower part of the *g* and the circles in the % symbol in most type designs.

The examiner should measure the size and proportion of all circle formations, and check them for irregularities in weight (see Point 7), for irregularities due to defects in the type face, and those formations filled in with ink.

Figure 82. Circle formations of various design.

Figure 83. Difference in design of oval in lower part of character.

POINT 12: SERIFS

Serifs are the miniature secondary bars or curves used to embellish the primary bar or curve of a letter. Like the initial and final strokes of handwriting, a systematic comparison of the serifs, or lack of serifs, on the characters of a questioned typewriting with those of the standard will give the examiner revealing evidence.

Differences in the design or location of a serif on certain characters will identify a particular make or model of a machine.

Figure 84. All three bars end with a serif at baseline.

m

Figure 85. Absence of serif.

m

Figure 86. No serifs at baseline.

M

Figure 87. Serifs at top and at baseline.

Figure 88. Absence of serifs.

1 1 1 1 1 1

Figure 89. Variation in length, angle and placement of serifs.

I

Figure 90. Absence of serifs.

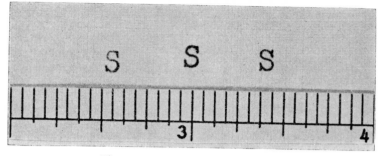

Figure 91. Distinguishing serifs.

S

Figure 92. Absence of serifs.

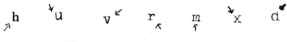

Figure 93. Defective serifs.

Being at the beginning or ending of strokes, a serif cast is especially vulnerable to breakage or distortion through wear and tear of the machine. These defects and irregularities can be prime factors in the identification of a particular machine, or of a questioned typewriting.

A photographic enlargement or a photomicrograph may be used to demonstrate the difference in design or irregularity in a serif.

Section 7

Conclusion

TYPEWRITING identification is based on the same principle underlying handwriting identification, or any other thing which has a great number of possible variations.

The identification of a typewritten document can be likened to the identification of a particular person. A person may be identified in general by his sex, size, features etc., and *in addition,* for example, by a radical mastectomy scar. A typewriter may be identified in general by characteristics such as type design and size, possessed by all machines of a specific make and model, and *in addition,* for example, by a flaw in the serif on the letter *E.*

No opinion as to identity should be based upon only a few dissimilarities (or similarities). It is the *combination* of measurements and characteristics which all together make up the conclusion.

When good, clear specimens are available in sufficient amount for a scientific identification of the twelve points of comparison, it is possible to show with absolute certainty that a document was, or was not, produced by a particular machine.

The mathematical probability of the same combination of these characteristics divergent from the norm appearing in two machines is practically nil. The evidence of the twelve points of comparison can be conclusive proof.

Section 8

Summary

SUMMED up, there are twelve points of comparison in typewriting identification just as there are twelve points of comparison in handwriting and fingerprint identification.

1. Uniformity
2. Irregularities
3. Size and proportion
4. Alignment
5. Spacing
6. Degree of slant
7. Weight of strokes
8. I-dots, periods, commas, quotation marks
9. Bars
10. Curves
11. Circle formations
12. Serifs.

PART II

PROOF OF THE FACT

Section 1

Reasons and Basis for Opinion

W HEN the examiner has finished his scientific analysis of the questioned and standard typewriting specimens, and has formed his conclusion as to whether the questioned document is genuine or a forgery, he must prepare his reasons and basis for opinion in such a manner that the judge and jury will also reach the same conclusion.

The value of the document examiner's opinion as evidence depends upon the proficiency and clarity with which he demonstrates its correctness. The best method of demonstrating the basis for his opinion is the use of photographs to report to the judge and jury the facts discovered by the typewriting examiner in his analysis.

Photographs appeal to the sense of sight. By presenting good, clear pictures of the twelve points of comparison, the examiner has a valuable tool which will help him perform the task of convincing the minds of those who are to decide the case in court.

Photographs are *permanent*. They make it possible to avoid the inadequacy of viewing fleeting pictures of the twelve points of comparison under magnification, and the almost impossible task of trying to keep the points in mind while another observer takes his turn at the magnifier as the examiner is making his comments.

Photographs are *objective*. Whereas the words of an examiner may carry prejudice, the camera lens records the twelve points of comparison with precision accurately and with entire objectivity. The objective photograph represents far better evidence than even the most detailed description.

Admitted as evidence in court, the value of photographs alone may be enough to prove the facts at issue.

Section 2

Forensic Photography

PHOTOGRAPHING documents requires special knowledge and equipment, and skill in techniques. The questioned document examiner is cautioned not to perform the photography himself, unless he has been specially trained for the work.

The examiner may have a foolproof case to report to the court, with his I.S.Q.T. twelve points of comparison, which is rendered useless because of unsatisfactory exhibits. A forensic, or document, photographer should be engaged to do the work.

By checking the yellow pages of the telephone book, or inquiring at his local police department or county crime lab, the typewriting examiner can usually locate a document photographer. There are now scientific identification technicians who are especially prepared to make photographs in relation to questioned documents.

An expert portrait photographer may not have the essential apparatus to photograph documents. Special lenses and other equipment are necessary to make detailed photographs showing distinctly each of the twelve points of comparison. Often typewriting is written with blue or other color ribbons, making it necessary to use color filters in order to obtain clear pictures.

Where the issue is whether or not an erasure was made on a document in question, the examiner can have the forensic photographer subject the suspected document to transmitted light, which will reveal overtyping.

A forensic photographer can determine accurately the

volume and angle of lighting required in a photographic illustration. For example, if the weight of the strokes is at issue, the angle of light used by the photographer is important. Also, a specimen made without a ribbon and photographed by side light will show the design of face type, and will bring out defective characters.

The typewriting examiner will be repaid more than the cost of securing the services of a forensic photographer in the superior exhibits he will have for his court demonstration. And he can be confident that the photographs will be admissible as evidence.

Section 3

Enlargements of Twelve Points of Comparison

TYPEWRITING in its natural size is too small to use for the examiner's demonstration in court. Properly enlarged photographs are indispensable to demonstrate and interpret the twelve points of comparison which the examiner has found in the exemplars to report.

Enlarged photographs made for exhibits enable the judge and jury to see for themselves the points of comparison, and to follow the technical report of the typewriting examiner as he is giving it. Whatever can be seen the mind can measure and compare.

For comparison, the typewriting in its natural size should be displayed beside its enlargement. When the examiner points out an otherwise unnoticeable characteristic, then

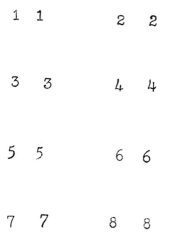

Figure 94. Variation in design of numbers in natural size.

shows its counterpart in its natural size, the observer can see the characteristic which he most likely hadn't seen before.

To make his alteration, an experienced forger may have

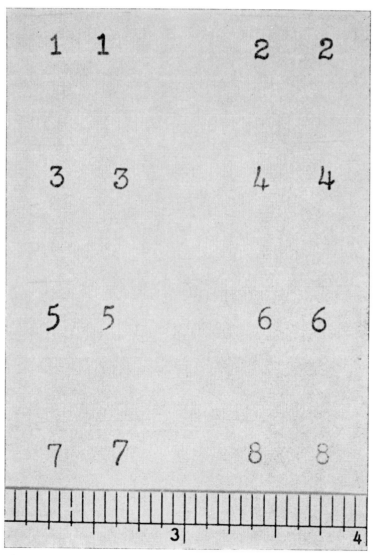

Figure 95. Enlargement showing variation in design of numbers.

selected a machine with characters very similar to those used in preparing the original document. But an enlargement of the specimens will reveal the differences when the individual characters are compared.

The microscopic difference in design of the comma or the numbers produced by the various makes and models of machines is almost imperceptible to the untrained eye. Their enlargement will reveal the distinction.

The uniform impressions produced by an electric typewriter, as opposed to a manually operated machine, is revealed by photographic enlargements.

The slant of the characters may be so slight as to go unnoticed until an enlargement of the specimen is made. The degree of slant, weight of strokes, and spacing can be measured and compared when the typewriting is enlarged.

Enlargement also enables the analyst to measure alignment. The perpendicular position of a character in relation to the baseline, for instance, is important in individualizing a machine (see Part I, Sec. 6, Point 4). This characteristic may not seem very prominent, but enlargement will bring it out clearly. Enlargement is also useful in measuring the parallelism of the lines.

Irregularities and defects in the characters become clear and more pronounced when the specimens are enlarged.

Figure 96. Defective characters in natural size.

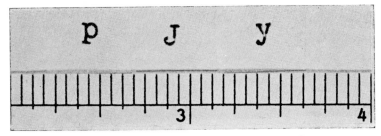

Figure 97. Enlargement showing defects in characters.

There is no set rule as to how many times a specimen should be enlarged but, as in the case of handwriting, usually typewriting should be enlarged four times its natural size. If the impressions are clean, strong, and even, it may be sufficient to enlarge the specimen only twice its natural size.

There are cases when enlarging four times may render the specimen less clear. For example, if the typewriting is dominated by breaks in the characters, which occurred when a worn ribbon was used, enlargement of four times may be excessive.

In some cases, photomicrographs are necessary to show the defects and irregularities more clearly. Photomicrographs are direct enlargements of specimens made by replacing the eyepiece of a microscope with a camera. In this type of enlargement, characteristics of a microscopic nature are reproduced as seen under the microscope.

The microscope or magnifying glass discovers the twelve points of comparison, but the photographic enlargement

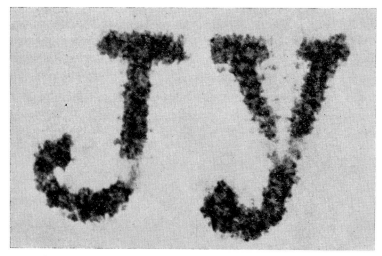

Figure 98. Photomicrographs showing defects in detail.

exhibits them to the observers. In court, an enlarged photograph is sometimes absolutely conclusive as evidence.

The enlarged photograph must be proved to be correct (see Sec. 10), and be admitted in evidence before the examiner may proceed with his demonstration.

Section 4

Duplicate Photographs

THE document examiner will have the forensic photographer make enough reproductions of the questioned and standard typewriting specimens, in their natural size and their enlargements, to use in the examiner's preparation and presentation of the facts in court.

Extra photographs will be needed to cut out from the questioned and standard typewriting the twelve points of comparison the analyst has found for the identification. These will be arranged side by side in parallel columns as described in Section 9 and illustrated in Figure 104. Without duplicate photographs the examiner's demonstration would be impossible without mutilating the document in question.

This composite photograph will be included with the duplicates of the questioned and standard typewriting, in their natural size and enlarged, in the sets provided for the observers (see Part II, Sec. 9).

In the usual case, because of the expense involved, it is not practical to provide individual sets for every member of the jury. Referred to here is the ideal example, which is rarely carried out in practice. Occasionally in a special case, where hundreds of thousands of dollars are involved, a set of duplicate photographs might be provided for each member of the jury, the judge, and the attorneys trying the case. Usually a set or two of the photographs passed among the jury is sufficient.

Individual exhibits afford the observers the opportunity to study and compare all the points at issue. They give those who are to decide the case a means of following the technical testimony as the examiner is giving it.

As expedient as it may seem to demonstrate a typewriting identification by projecting it onto a screen, this method is not recommended for use in court. An individual exhibit which the observer can hold in his hands at his usual reading level is far more effective. This affords him close observation, allowing him to take the time he needs to study each of the twelve points of comparison at his own rate of speed.

The examiner of course will want a set of photographs for himself to use as charts for his court demonstration, and duplicates to be admitted in evidence.

Section 5

Markings on Photographs

BEFORE the examiner takes the photographs of his type-writing specimens into court, it is important that he place his mark of identification (a symbol or his initials) on the back of each one. Each photograph should also carry the forensic photographer's mark of identification.

Outside of these markings on the back, no photograph introduced in court as evidence may contain marking of any kind. A photograph is a self-explanatory illustration, and should contain no markings which are not part of the photograph, or of the original typewriting which it represents.

Arrows, numbers, letters, underlining, dates, initials—any type of identification mark on the face of a photograph —will cause it to lose its character as a photograph. Defaced, it will depreciate in value and in most cases be useless as evidence.

To number the twelve points of comparison and show them graphically with small arrows, the examiner can mark a duplicate photograph to be used as a chart or offered in evidence for identification only.

Specimens may be photographed with superimposed transparent measuring devices, a method which does not constitute marking. For example, when the degree of slant of a type-writing is an essential point of comparison, the specimen may be photographed with a superimposed plastic protractor (see Fig. 62). Or a specimen may be photographed with a template of ruled squares placed over the letters to show alignment or misalignment (Fig. 27).

Although this method does not constitute marking, and

does not destroy the admissibility of the photograph as evidence, such an exhibit received in evidence will be marked by an officer of the court, "for identification." It will then be accepted in evidence for identification only.

Photostatic Photographs

As with handwritten questioned documents, photostatic photographs, i.e. photographs made by a photographic copying machine (like xerography), are almost useless in questioned typewriting investigation.

In some cases, photostatic photographs are actually misleading and should not be solely depended upon in the investigation or as illustrations for demonstrating the fact.

This type of photograph tends to hide certain defects and significant evidences of forgery. In the photostatic process much detail is lost.

Slight variations in the style of type face, and imperfections and irregularities in the faces, may be concealed in a photostatic photograph. Detailed differences in the design of i-dots, periods, and commas are lost in the process of photostating.

The weight of the strokes of a typewriting may be indistinguishable in photostatic photographs. The footing of a typewriting, if it is heavy on one of its sides, or "off its feet," may be concealed. The shading of the strokes, like that produced by the IBM typewriter, is also lost. Fine, medium, and thick strokes are shown in one flat shade making them look alike and covering up evidence which may be important to the case.

Serifs—embellishments on the type—which give the examiner especially revealing evidence, do not appear distinctly in every detail in this type of photograph. Defects and irregularities in serifs can be prime factors in identification, and it is important that they be photographed clearly and accurately.

Photostatic photographs are sufficient for recording the subject matter of a document, but they are not satisfactory in questioned typewriting investigation.

Section 7

Identification From Carbon Copies

CARBON copies are popularly thought of as copies of the original typewriting. They are not. Both the original page and the carbon duplicate are originals. The carbon copy is not copied but is written in the same operation by the same operator on the same machine.

Often forgery can be proved by the carbon copy of a typewriting by the dissimilarity of impressions when compared with the original. Dissimilarities in the style of type, or certain defects in the characters found in one and not the other, will show the typewriting was produced on two different machines.

An interruption in the continuity of a typewritten document may be shown by variations in the carbon copy. It is difficult to reinsert precisely a page in a machine, and even more difficult to reinsert interleaving sheets of paper and carbon paper. Measurement will disclose variations in margin alignment, and in the vertical and horizontal spacing and alignment of the characters.

If the carbon copy contains words or figures which are different from the original, or contains additional words or figures, it will indicate forgery.

An original page of a document with a change made in it may be submitted which is purported to be authentic. By producing a carbon copy of the document containing no such change, having proved both documents to have been written on the same machine by the same operator in the same operation, the examiner can determine that the questioned alteration was done fraudulently.

$185,000

the ~~$85,000~~ and all my

including the Indian rugs,

to Laurella E. Kusel.

Figure 99. Original document carrying a change purported to be authentic.

the $85,000 and all my

including the Indian rugs,

to Laurella E. Kusel.

Figure 100. Carbon copy of same document.

One persimmon, two
persimmon, three
persimmon four.
Old soldier Jed.

Figure 101. Questioned carbon copy.

One persimmon, two
persimmon, three
persimmon four.
Old soldier Jed.

Figure 102. Standard original.

Where there are several carbon copy pages constituting a document, a variation in the color of the typewriting, due to the use of a different sheet of carbon paper, may be noticeable. Since only a slight variation in color may go unnoticed, the examiner should submit the suspicious carbon pages to a scientific identification technician for color tests.

Should a document containing several pages have a carbon

copy substituted for one of the original pages, the examiner should question the authenticity of the carbon copy.

In analyzing a carbon copy, the examiner will follow the same principles and procedure used in analyzing an original page. He will reduce the typewriting to its basic strokes and make a careful scientific comparison—stroke by stroke —of the questioned with the standard, guided by the I.S.Q.T. method with its twelve points of comparison.

Section 8

Mounting Exhibits

THE photographs which are prepared for use in court as exhibits should be properly mounted so that they will lie flat and not buckle.

Some examiners recently have returned to the old method of having photographs mounted with a dry backing cloth. Attorneys as well as examiners find this type of backing convenient for jotting notes pertaining to the specimen. A stamped identification mark will remain on the back of the photograph even though the backing has been peeled from it.

Photographs should be mounted with just enough border to allow the necessary data for identifying the exhibit, since the photographs themselves must not be marked in any way.

The mounting will contain the numbers of the exhibits arranged in their order—e.g. Q-1, Q-2, on the questioned typewriting, and S-1, S-2, S-3, S-4, on the standards. Dates to show successive specimens will also appear on the border of the mounting.

To save time and confusion, before the examiner takes them into court the exhibits should be marked and arranged in the order in which each is to be presented. Placed *separately* in a Manila folder or envelope, they should be given to the observer as a complete set before the trial begins so as to eliminate any unnecessary interruptions during the demonstration.

It is important that the set of exhibits are not bound together. Separate photographs allow side by side comparison of the questioned and standard typewriting.

The exhibits should be of a size that can be conveniently

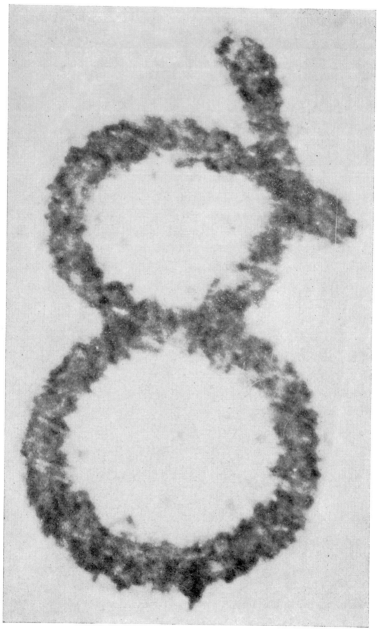

Figure 103. An overwhelming illustration of one of the twelve points of comparison.

handled by the judge, jury, and attorneys involved in the case. They must be large enough to show clearly the twelve points of comparison, but not larger than they can be seen all at once at normal reading distance. A standard 11 by 14 inch photograph is an adequate size.

Exhibits which are to be used as charts in the demonstration should be 20 by 24 inches in size. These will include enlargements of the entire specimens of the questioned and standard typewriting, for the observers to follow graphically the examiner's statements, as well as individual 20 by 24 inch charts of each of the twelve points of comparison. The more overwhelming the display, the more effective the testimony.

Section 9

Classification of Twelve Points of Comparison

STANDARDS—i.e. typewriting specimens that have been proved to be authentic—are necessary for the examiner to compare with a questioned typewriting and classify his twelve points of comparison.

Evidence must be based on at least these twelve points—a sufficient number of characteristics to prove identification—and these twelve characteristics must be presented in a form that makes them perceptible and distinctive to those observers who are to decide the matter in court.

Few jurors will notice any particular difference in the characters of one typewriting from another, even though they may have seen typewriting every day. Their untrained eyes see the typewriting in only a general way as letters and numbers, but do not see it in a specific way so as to make a distinction between one style of type face and another. They do not readily perceive defects or irregularities in the characters.

Although the examiner will be pointing out these differences (or similarities) during his demonstration, the observers will have a difficult time carrying in their minds points of comparison from one specimen to another unless these points are placed close enough together for a side by side comparison.

The twelve points of comparison can be cut out from the duplicate photographs of the questioned and standard typewriting specimens and placed side by side in parallel columns. Classified in this position, the points that differ, or are alike, will appear distinctly and will be seen at once by the

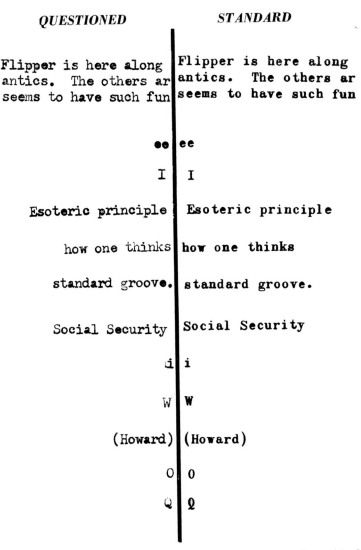

QUESTIONED **STANDARD**

Flipper is here along Flipper is here along
antics. The others ar antics. The others ar
seems to have such fun seems to have such fun

ee ee

I I

Esoteric principle Esoteric principle

how one thinks how one thinks

standard groove. standard groove.

Social Security Social Security

i i

W W

(Howard) (Howard)

O O

Q Q

Figure 104. Classification of twelve points of comparison side by side in parallel columns: (1) Uniformity, (2) Irregularities, (3) Size and Proportion, (4) Alignment, (5) Spacing, (6) Degree of Slant, (7) Weight of Strokes, (8) I-dots, Periods, Commas, Quotation Marks, (9) Bars, (10) Curves, (11) Circle Formations, (12) Serifs.

observer. The instant comparison eliminates the necessity of switching his eyes from one photograph to another in his attempt to form a mental picture of a point of comparison.

The observer cannot make these photographic groupings himself. The examiner must do it for him. If the observer had to leave one photograph and take up another, to study all the points of comparison, he could not retain the images of the characteristics. For him to study the twelve points of comparison, in determining their similarity or dissimilarity, they must be placed side by side in one exhibit so that he can see the whole group at one time while the examiner points out the characteristics.

After he has studied the twelve points of comparison side by side in the cut-apart photographs, the observer can compare them with the original specimens of questioned and standard typewriting available in the individual set of exhibits.

The classification of the twelve points of comparison, by cutting them apart and placing them side by side in parallel columns, is an essential part of the typewriting examiner's demonstration in court.

Section 10

Admissible as Evidence

BECAUSE a typewriter records its individuality in the documents which it produces, leaving definite factors of identification, typewriting is admissible as evidence to prove whether a questioned document is genuine or a forgery.

The basis for admissibility of typewriting is the fact that a typewriter, after it has been used over a period of time, develops certain distinguishable characteristics in its type face which are recorded in the work it produces. Typewriting also reflects the habits of the operator who produced it (see Part I, Sec. 3), and these factors are admissible as evidence.

Specimens are essential, and when offered as evidence they must be proved to be satisfactory. The original documents must be carefully preserved in order not to jeopardize their value as evidence. The examiner must make sure that the specimens are not rejected on grounds that they have been tampered with and are not in their original condition.

Photographs Admissible as Evidence

Photographs are admissible as evidence so long as they have been proved to be correct reproductions of the original typewriting specimens.

In the hands of a competent document photographer, camera lenses in use today make photographic reproductions absolutely accurate. To be admissible as evidence a print must be free of all defects and distortion. Even the slightest imperfection will render it inadmissible, as it presents a false representation of the facts.

A correct photograph is sharp, shows distinctly the twelve points of comparison and other necessary details, and is free from marking of any kind (see Part II, Sec. 5). Marks weaken the evidential value of a photograph, and endanger its admissibility.

Proving a Photograph

A photograph is proved to be correct when the photographer who made it testifies that he made it, that he is qualified to make document photographs, and that the one he has made is correct. His initials, or other mark of identification, should appear on the back of it.

If the photographer who made the photograph is not available, another qualified photographer can testify that he has compared the negative with the original document and found it to be an accurate reproduction of it; and that he has examined the print and found it to be an accurate copy of the negative.

Enlarged and Composite Photographs

Enlarged photographs, and composite photographs of the twelve points of comparison (Sec. 9), are admissible as evidence when proved authentic. These will be marked "for identification" by an officer of the court at the time they are admitted, and will be accepted in evidence for identification only.

Photostatic Photographs

In most cases the court will not allow the admissibility of photostatic photographs as evidence. However, if the judge makes an exception due to the circumstances of the case, the Photostat must be proved to be a correct and direct copy of the original document. It must not be a photostatic copy of a Photostat.

When a Photostat is made of a Photostat, subsequent copies gradually eliminate paper connections. Because of this, another document altogether different from the original can be made by substituting other typewriting in place of that which was originally there.

Carbon Copies

When a carbon copy is a distinct duplicate of the original typewriting, produced at the same time and on the same machine, it is admissible as evidence. Such a copy is considered to be an original, and is primary evidence admissible without accounting for the other copy.

The slightest alteration in a duplicate carbon is material. Errors corrected or overtyped destroy the value of a carbon copy and render it inadmissible as evidence.

Section 11

Presentation in Court of the Proof of the Fact

THE examiner's testimony and presentation in court in a questioned typewriting case is much the same as that in questioned handwriting. It is based on the scientific comparison of the questioned typewriting with the known standards, and the examiner's opinion as to whether the questioned writing is genuine or forged.

Sometimes the question is merely to determine whether a document was written on a certain kind of machine. Sometimes it is a matter of determining whether a document was written on one particular machine out of several suspected ones. Again, the question may be only one of ascertaining the date when the document was typewritten, or if the document was written continuously in one operation or at different times.

Although typewriting questions vary according to the circumstances of each case, the most important points of consideration are the class characteristics and the individual characteristics of the typewriting.

Class characteristics are those characteristics appearing in the typewriting which are common to all machines of a certain make and model (Olympia, Remington, Smith-Corona, etc.). *Individual characteristics* are those peculiar variations produced by a particular machine after it has been in use for some time (defects in type faces, faulty alignment, etc.).

In court with his carefully prepared exhibits, after the examiner has shown—with a stroke by stroke comparison—that the questioned typewriting came from a certain make and model machine, he will proceed with his twelve points of comparison to demonstrate the similarities or dissimilarities between the questioned typewriting and the standards.

The value of his demonstration will depend upon the clarity of his exhibits (see Part II, Sec. 1). In addition to his presentation of the twelve points of comparison set forth in his exhibit of their side by side classification (Sec. 9), he will give a systematic recount of the facts discovered during his precourt study of the exemplars.

Each fact stated orally will be supported by the examiner's visual exhibits. The examiner's testimony, which is usually unfamiliar to the juror, is better understood from the observation of photographic exhibits than from the examiner's oral statements.

The evidence, based on the twelve points of comparison to prove identification, must be clear and perceptible so that the observers can arrive at the conclusion to which the examiner has been leading them.

After his statement of the facts supported by photographic illustration, the examiner should explain the principle underlying the identification of questioned typewriting. As in the case of anything which has a large number of possible variations, the identity is made by a systematic comparison of all the elements which all together constitute the conclusion.

It should be emphasized that it is the *combination of characteristics* that helps identify a typewriting—a combination mathematically beyond mere chance.

Section 12

Conclusion

No one book can exhaust the subject of typewriting identification, especially one the length of this manual.

I.S.Q.T. purposely presents typewriting identification in a very simplified way. An attorney does not have the time, and does not need, to pour through page after page of the material which has been written on typewriting identification, some of which is interesting but irrelevant.

There are several books on the market in which one can pursue the subject in greater depth, but it is hoped that this presentation will be helpful as a handbook for the typewriting investigator and as a guide for the attorney handling a questioned typewriting case.

Although this manual may be helpful to examiners using other systems of typewriting investigation, the primary purpose of I.S.Q.T. is to set forth an original system of typewriting identification—a scientific method of the discovery of the fact and the proving of it.

This system is based on the method of reducing typewriting to its two basic strokes—the straight stroke (bar), and the curve—followed by the scientific analysis of these two strokes.

The same principles of identification found in I.S.Q.D., which deals with handwriting identification, are applicable to typewriting identification. These scientific principles are founded on Graphoanalysis, which has had over a half century of research and experiment.

Guided by the I.S.Q.T. system, an investigator should be able to apply the basic principles of *observation* and analysis of individual strokes to any questioned typewriting and be as sure of his opinion as a fingerprint expert is sure of his conclusion.

Bibliography

1. BAKER, J. NEWTON: *Law of Disputed and Forged Documents.* Charlottesville, Michie, 1955.

2. BATES, BILLY PRIOR: *I.S.Q.D. Identification System for Questioned Documents.* Springfield, Thomas, 1970.

3. BUNKER, M. N.: *Graphoanalysis: Post Graduate Course, Lecture 16.* Springfield, I.G.A.S., 1960.

4. COOKE, T. DICKERSON: *The Blue Book of Crime,* 24th ed. Chicago, Applied Science, 1961.

5. Department of Justice: *The FBI Laboratory.* Washington, U.S. Government Printing Office, 1969 (revised).

6. Editorial staffs of Bancroft-Whitney Company: *American Jurisprudence Proof of Facts Annotated·* Rochester, Lawyer's Co-operative, 1959, vol. 1, 16.

7. Editorial staffs of Bancroft-Whitney Company: *American Jurisprudence/State & Federal,* 2nd ed. Rochester, Lawyer's Co-operative, 1967, vol. 29.

8. Hilton, Ordway: *Scientific Examination of Questioned Documents.* Chicago· Callaghan, 1956.

9. Osborn, Albert S.: *Questioned Documents,* 2nd ed. Albany, Boyd, 1929.

Index

A

Absolute identification, 59
Additions to docuents, 43
Adjacent characters, alignment of, 28, 36
Alignment
  baseline, 28, 32, 36
  factor in identification, 20, 27-32
  horizontal, 28
  IBM typewriter, 31-32
  imaginary square, 29
  irregularities in, 20, 28-32
  measurement of, 29, 69
  quality of typewriting, 20
  of adjacent characters, 28
  uniformity in, 28
  vertical, 28
Angle of light, 65-66
Apostrophes, 47
Arrangement of subject matter on page, 13, 19-20

B

Backing cloth, 81
Bars
  angle at which joined, 50
  basic strokes, 18, 49-50
  combined with other strokes, 50
  determining slant, 52
  distance from baseline, 50-51
  factor in identification, 49-52
  irregularities in, 52
  length of, 50-51
  measurement of, 50
  serve as staff, 49
  size and proportion of, 52
  weight of, 50, 52
Baseline, irregularities in, 28, 32, 36
Basic strokes, 18, 49-50, 52-54
Basis of examiner's opinion, 90-91

Battered or broken type faces, 21
Bent type bars, 36
Block system, 35, 36
Borders, 81
Burs, 43

C

Capitals, incorrect use of, 13
Carbon copies
  admissible as evidence, 89
  alterations in, 89
  as originals, 78
  discontinuity of typewriting shown by, 78
  forgery proved by, 78
  irregularities in, 78
  procedure for analyzing, 80
  substituted for originals, 79-80
  test by scientific identification technician, 79
  twelve points of comparison, 80
  variation in color of, 79
Characteristics
  class, 90
  classification of, 84-86
  combination of, 91
  conspicuous, 19
  inconspicuous, 19
  individual, 90
Charts, *see* Exhibits
Circle formations
  combined with other strokes, 55-56
  factor in identification, 55-56
  irregularities in, 56
  measurement of, 56
  related to curves, 55
  size and proportion of, 56
  variation in design of, 56
  weight of, 56
Class characteristics, 90

Classification, twelve points of comparison, 84-86
Clues to identification, 19
Colloquialisms, 13
Colons, 46
Color filters, 65
Combination of basic strokes, 18, 50, 52-55
Combination of characteristics, 59, 91
Commas, 47-48, 69
Composite photographs, 84-86, 88
Conspicuous characteristics, 19
Continuous typewriting, 16
Curves
  absence of, 54
  basic strokes, 52-54
  combined with other strokes, 52-55
  factor in identification, 52-55
  irregularities in, 54
  measurement of, 54
  shapes of, 53-55
  size and proportion of, 54
  weight of, 54
Cut-apart photographs, 84-86

D

Date of typewriting
  establishment of, 15-17
  marked on border, 81
Defects, 19-24, 36
Degree of slant, *see* Slant
Dents, 21
Dirty type faces, 19, 24
Discontinuous typewriting
  a suspicion of fraud, 16
  how shown, 16, 29-31, 35, 43, 78
Document photographer, 65-66
Duplicate photographs
  admitted in evidence, 73
  as charts, 73, 74
  as identification evidence, 74-75
  cut-apart, 84
  individual exhibits, 72-73, 81, 83, 86
  markings on, 74
  necessity of, 72

number required, 72-73
twelve points of comparison, 72, 84

E

Electric typewriter, 13, 42, 69
Elite type, 25
Enlargements
  admissible as evidence, 88
  conclusive as evidence, 71
  degree of, 70
  factors revealed in, 69
  inconspicuous characteristics revealed in, 67-69
  indispensable for court presentation, 67
  measurement from, 69
  preferable to natural size, 67
  serifs, 58
  twelve points of comparison, 70-71
Erasures, 65
Evidence
  admissibility of photographs, 66, 87-88
  admissibility of typewriting, 87
  carbon copies, 89
  composite photographs, 88
  duplicate photographs, 73
  enlargements, 88
  "for identification," 88
  markings on photographs, 88
  photostats, 88-89
  proving a photograph, 88
  superimposed measuring devices, 74-75
  twelve points of comparison, 84
Examiner's mark of identification, 74
Examiner's testimony, 90-91
Excessive ink in ribbon, 19, 24, 42
Exhibits
  arranged in advance, 81
  as charts, 73, 83
  individual, 72-73, 81, 83, 86
  marking, 81
  mounting, 81
  numbering, 81

overwhelming display, 82-83
side by side comparison of, 81
size of, 81-83
twelve points of comparison, 73
unbound sets, 81

F

FBI laboratory, 8
Fingerprint identification, 18, 60, 93
Footing of typewriting, 39
"For identification," 74-75, 88
Forensic photographer, 65-66
Fundamental strokes, 18

G

General appearance of typewriting, 19-21
Graphoanalysis, 92

H

Habits of operator, 13, 32-34
Handwriting identification, V, 5-6, 18, 19, 40, 50, 55, 57, 59, 60, 90, 92
History of individual typewriter, 17
Horizontal alignment, 12, 20, 32
Hunt and peck system, 12-13, 42-43
Hyphens, 27

I

IBM typewriters, 8, 31, 39
Identification, *see* Typewriting identification
Idiosyncracies of operator, 13, 24
Individual touch, 12-13, 42-43
I-dots
    distinguishing characteristics, 43-46
    magnification of, 44
    position in relation to stem, 45-46
Imaginary square, 29, 35
Inconspicuous characteristics, 19, 67-69
Individual characteristics, 90
Individual exhibits, 72-73, 81, 83, 86
Individual history of typewriters, 17
Individual touch, 12-13, 20, 42-43

Individuality of operator, 12-14, 24
Inexperienced typist, 34
Interlineations, 15, 43
Irregularities
    alignment, 20, 28-32
    baseline, 20
    carbon copies, 78
    caused by machine, 19-24, 35-36
    caused by operator, 13, 22-25, 32, 34-35
    concealed in photostats, 76
    determination of date, 16
    factor in identification, 19-25, 28-32, 34-37, 69, 78
    major cause of, 22-23
    revealed by enlargement, 69
    serifs, 58, 76
    slant, 36-37
    spacing, 34-36
I.S.Q.D. principles applicable, V, 92
I.S.Q.T.
    basis of system, 92
    guide for attorneys, 92
    laboratory basis of, 18, 19
    original system, 92
    simplified presentation, 92

J

J-dots, 46

L

Laboratory basis of I.S.Q.T., 18, 19
Line spacings, 16
Lint in type faces, 24
Loose type bars, 23

M

Make of machine, 7
Manufacturing companies, 7-8
Margins, 13, 16, 20, 32
Markings
    destroy evidence, 74
    duplicate photographs, 74
    examiner's identification, 74
    "for identification," 74-75
    on border, 81

photographer's identification, 74, 88
superimposed measuring devices, 74-75
Measurement
  alignment, 29, 69
  bars, 50
  circle formations, 56
  curves, 54
  enlargements, 69
  size and proportion, 26-27
  slant, 37-38
  spacing, 32-33, 35, 69
  weight of strokes, 40
Misalignment
  caused by machine, 29, 32, 36
  caused by operator, 12, 29, 32
  how shown, 29-32
Modification of documents, 15, 43
Mounting exhibits, 73, 81-83
Muddiness
  caused by ribbon, 24
  caused by type faces, 24
  only certain characters, 24
  overall characters, 24

N

Nicked type faces, 19
Numbering exhibits, 81
Numbers
  alteration of, 25
  distinguishing styles of, 25, 67
  enlargement of, 68-69

O

Objectivity of photographs, 63
Observation, 93
"Off its feet," 39
"On its feet," 39
Operator
  electric typewriter, 13
  factors in identification of, 12-14, 48
  habits of, 13, 32-34
  identification of, 12-14
  idiosyncracies of, 13, 24
  individuality of, 12-14, 24

inexperienced, 12-13, 34
irregularities caused by, 22-25, 32, 34-35
misalignment caused by, 29, 32
semiskilled, 12
skilled, 12
speed of, 12-13
spelling, 13
touch of, 12
Oral testimony, 91
Overtyping, 65
Overwhelming exhibits, 82-83

P

Paragraph indentations, 13, 20, 33
Parallelism of lines, 16, 69
Parentheses, 27, 53, 54
Particular machine, 10-11
Periods
  changing to comma, 47-48
  distinguishing characteristics, 43-44
  misuse by operator, 48
Permanency of photographs, 63
Personal nature of typewritten documents, 14
Photographer
  document or forensic, 65-66
  mark of identification, 74, 88
Photographs
  accuracy of reproduction, 87
  admissible as evidence, 66, 87-88
  appeal to sense of sight, 63
  as charts, 73, 83
  basis for opinion, 63
  composite, 84-86, 88
  cut-apart, 84-86
  duplicate, 84
  enlargements, 58, 67-69, 70-71, 83, 88
  examiner's mark of identification on, 74
  imperfections in, 87
  individual exhibits, 81, 86
  markings on, 74-75, 88
  mounting, 81-83
  objectivity of, 63

overwhelming exhibits, 82-83
permanency of, 63
photographer's mark of identification on, 88
photostatic, 76-77, 88-89
preferable to oral testimony, 63-64
proof of facts, 64
proving, 88
reporting to judge and jury, 63
side by side comparison of, 81, 84-86
size of exhibits, 81-83
superimposed measuring devices on, 74-75
xerography, 76
Photography
  color filters, 65
  erasures, 65
  overtyping, 65
  scientific identification technician, 65
  side light, 66
  transmitted light, 65
  typing without ribbon, 66
Photomicrographs
  how made, 70
  microscopic characteristics revealed in, 70
  serifs, 58
Photostatic photographs
  admissible as evidence, 88-89
  allowed by judge, 88-89
  conceal evidence, 76
  not satisfactory in typewriting identification, 76-77
  proved to be correct, 88-89
Pica type, 25
Pinched typewriting, 31, 35
Platen, 27-28, 43
Precision ruler, 26, 40
Projection on screen, 73
Proportional type, 26, 31, 35
Protractor, 37-38
Proving photographs, 88
Punctuation, 13, 19, 32-34, 48

Q

Quality of typewriting, 12-14, 19-20, 38-43
Questioned typewriting, first step in examination of, 19
Quotation marks, 47-48

R

Record of makes and models, manufacturing companies, 7-8
Record of styles of type, FBI laboratory, 8
Record of type face changes
  determination of date, 16
  manufacturing companies, 7-8
Reinsertion of paper, 16, 29-31, 35
Reporting to judge and jury, 63, 90-91
Ribbon
  discontinuous typewriting, 43
  excessive ink in, 19, 24, 42
  muddiness, 24
  weight of strokes, 43

S

Scars, 21, 23
Scientific identification technician, 65, 79
Semicolons, 46
Sentence construction, 13
Serifs
  absence of, 57, 58
  definition of, 57
  enlargement of, 58
  factor in identification, 57-58, 76
  irregularities in, 58, 76
  location on characters, 57
  photomicrographs of, 58
  revealing evidence, 57, 76
  variation in design of, 57
  vulnerability of, 58
Shading, 38-43
Skilled operator, 12
Side by side comparison, 72, 81, 84-86
Side light, 66
Size and proportion

factor in identification, 25-27
measurement of, 26-27
side by side comparison of, 85
styles of type, 25-27
Size of exhibits, 81-83
Slant
caused by machine, 37
caused by operator, 37
degree of, 36-37
factor in identification, 36-38
in relation to adjacent characters, 36
in relation to baseline, 36
measurement of, 37-38
permanent characteristic, 37
revealed in enlargement, 69
Smudged typewriting, 19, 24
Spacing
between letters and words, 35
between lines, 35
block system, 35
factor in identification, 13, 20, 31-33, 35, 36, 69, 85
imaginary square, 35
irregularities caused by machine, 32, 36
irregularities caused by operator, 13, 32
margins, 32
measurement of, 32-33, 35, 69
paragraph indentations, 33
proportional type, 31, 35
side by side comparison of, 85
uniformity of, 20
variable, 31, 35
Speed, 20
Spelling, 13
Stamped identification mark, 81
Straight stroke, 18
Strikeovers, 20
Striking force, 12, 20, 38, 40, 42-43
Styles of type
distinction lost in photostats, 76
distinction revealed in enlargements, 69
example of change in, 10

prevailing factors in identification, 9, 25-27
record of, 7-8
successive specimens, 17, 81
Successive specimens, 17, 81
Superimposed measuring devices, 74-75
Symmetrical typewriting, 35

T

T-bars, 50-51
Technician, scientific identification, 65
Testimony, examiner's, 90-91
Thickness of strokes, 38-43
Touch of operator, 12
Touch system, 42
Transmitted light, 65
Twelve points of comparison
basis of examiner's opinion, 90-91
carbon copies, 80
classification of, 84-86
enlargements of, 70-71
evidence based on, 84
examiner's testimony, 91
listed, 60
side by side comparison of, 72, 84-86
Type bars, 23
Type faces
irregularities in, 19-24, 36
record of styles, 7-8
Type-heads, 8-9
Typewriters
electric, 13, 42, 69
IBM, 8, 31, 39
identifiable characteristics, 5
individual history of, 17
make of machine, 7
manufacturing companies, 7-8
no two exactly alike, 7
Typewriting
admissible as evidence, 87-89
arrangement on page, 13, 19-20
basis for admissibility, 87
footing of, 39
microscopic examination of, 25

muddy, 24
"off its feet," 39
"on its feet," 39
pinched, 31, 35
quality of, 12, 19-20, 38-43
reduced to basic strokes, 52, 54
smudged, 19, 24
symmetrical, 35
unbalanced, 20
uniformity of, 19
Typewriting identification
  absolute, 59
  compared to fingerprint identification, 18, 60, 93
  compared to handwriting identification, V, 5-6, 18, 19, 40, 50, 55, 57, 59, 60, 90, 92
  essential parts of, V
  first step in, 5
  I.S.Q.D. principles applicable to, V, 92
  laboratory basis of, 18, 19
  principles underlying, 5, 59, 91
Typewriting protractor, 37-38
Typewritten documents
  ascertaining genuineness of, 16
  interlineations in, 15
  modification of, 15
  personal nature of, 14
  written at different times, 16
  written continuously in one operation, 16
Typing without ribbon, 66

U

Unbalanced typewriting, 20
Unbound sets, 81
Uniformity, 19-20
Untidiness, 20

V

Variable spacing, 31, 35
Variable weight
  caused by machine, 39-40
  caused by operator, 40, 42
  caused by ribbon, 39-40, 43
Vertical alignment, 16, 28-31

W

Warped type bars, 23, 36
Weight of strokes
  additions to documents identified by, 43
  burs, 43
  caused by machine, 39, 42, 43
  caused by operator, 12, 20, 38, 40, 42-43
  caused by ribbon, 43
  electric typewriter, 42
  factor in identification, 20, 38-43, 66, 69
  fraudulent alterations identified by, 43
  hunt and peck system, 42-43
  individual touch, 12-13, 42-43
  interlineations identified by, 43
  measurement of, 40
  "off its feet," 39
  revealed by angle of light, 66
  revealed in enlargement, 69
  shading (thickness), 38-43
  striking force, 12, 20, 38, 40, 42-43
  touch system, 42
  two aspects of, 38
  uniformity in, 20
  variable, 39
Wording of document, 13
Worn type faces, 19, 21

X

Xerography, 76